This book belongs to

. . . .

cat

lemon

clock

My First Phonics is a simple introduction to reading and writing. Each page features just one sound, and the sound is always picked out in a bright colour, making them easily recognisable. The book also focuses on the high-frequency and key words that children need to learn at reception level.

First published 2011 by Brown Watson
The Old Mill, 76 Fleckney Road,
Kibworth Beauchamp, Leic LE8 0HG

ISBN: 978-0-7097-1928-1

bee

My First Phonics

ENGLAND

a

apple

bag

cat

i

insects

hill

dig

e

elephant

wet

bed

O

dog

frog

cot

U

sun

cup

jump

f

fairy

fast

family

t

toys

tree

train

n

night

net

nurse

S

snow

sand

sails

r

rabbit

run

rug

h

house

hand

hen

l

lamp

leg

lemon

d

dragon

dad

dance

C

cow

carrots

car

ee

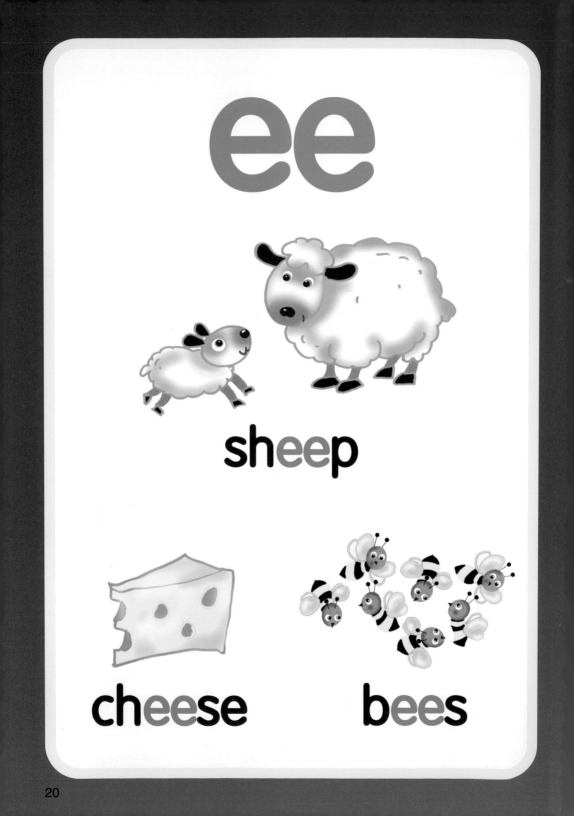

sheep

cheese

bees

oo

moon

spoon

boot

sh

shop

ship   **sh**oe

th

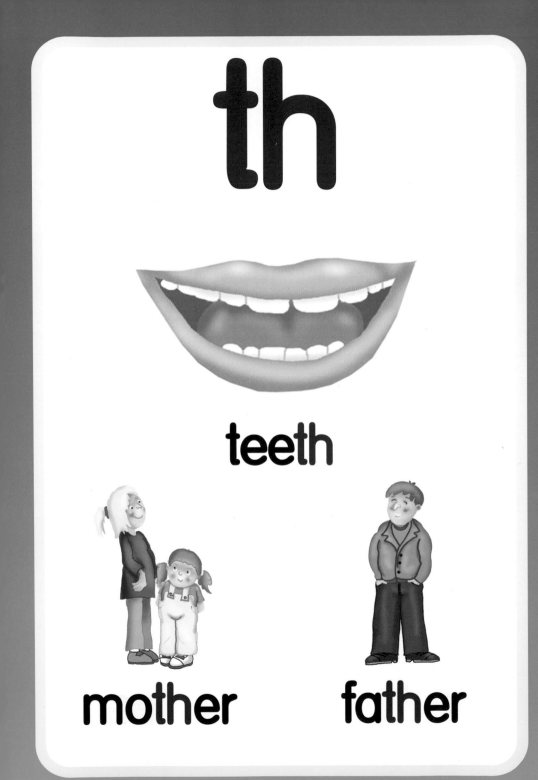

teeth

mother   father

ck

duck

clock

truck

ch

children

cherry

chair

cl

clown

clothes

clap

ll

ball

balloon

jelly

Join the letters and their different sounds to make words.

h a t

t e d

s i t

h o t

b u s

b e e

Santa

shed

fish

sock

duck

goose